BIBLE TALES

from the
Old Testament

Ward Lock Limited · London

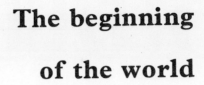

The beginning
of the world

The Bible begins by telling us how God created the heaven and the earth. This wonderful story of creation took seven days and upon each of the seven days God made a special part of heaven and earth.

On the first day of creation God made the light and the darkness. And on the days that followed He made every wonderful thing that lives in the universe. He made the heaven, the earth and the seas; the grass, the flowers and the trees; the sun, the moon and the stars. After He had created these God then made the fish, and the birds and the animals. On the sixth day God created man and woman.

When God saw everything that He had made, He saw that it was very good. On the Seventh day God ended this great work. God blessed this day and it is the one that we call Sunday.

The Story
of Noah

Many years after the world had been created, God saw that men and women were not living as He desired. This displeased Him greatly and He decided to send a great flood to destroy all the people. Everyone, that is, except Noah, a man who had pleased God well.

God warned Noah of the flood that was coming and told him to make a great boat, or ark as it was called. When the floods came, this wonderful ark was to shelter Noah, his family, and either two or seven of every kind of animal and bird that lived in the world.

At last the great ark was finished and the floods came. God shut Noah and his precious cargo safely inside the ark and the floods covered the earth for forty days. Every living thing except those in the ark was destroyed. Finally the floods went down and Noah came out of the ark and praised God. And so it was that all that was good was kept alive.

Jacob's dream

Jacob was the son of a man of great wisdom named Isaac. When Isaac was nearing the end of his life, Jacob quarrelled with his brother Esau and to escape Esau's anger Jacob went to visit an uncle far away. The journey was a long one and when the sun went down Jacob made a pillow from the stones that lay about on the ground. Then he lay down to sleep. It was whilst he

slept that a wonderful dream came to him. Jacob saw a great ladder which reached up to the heavens themselves, and going up and down it were the angels of God. And above these still stood the Lord.

God told Jacob that the country in which he slept would be given to the race of people to which Jacob belonged, the Hebrews. God also promised that He would always be with Jacob. When Jacob awoke he knew that God was in this marvellous place, and he set up his stone pillow to mark it forever.

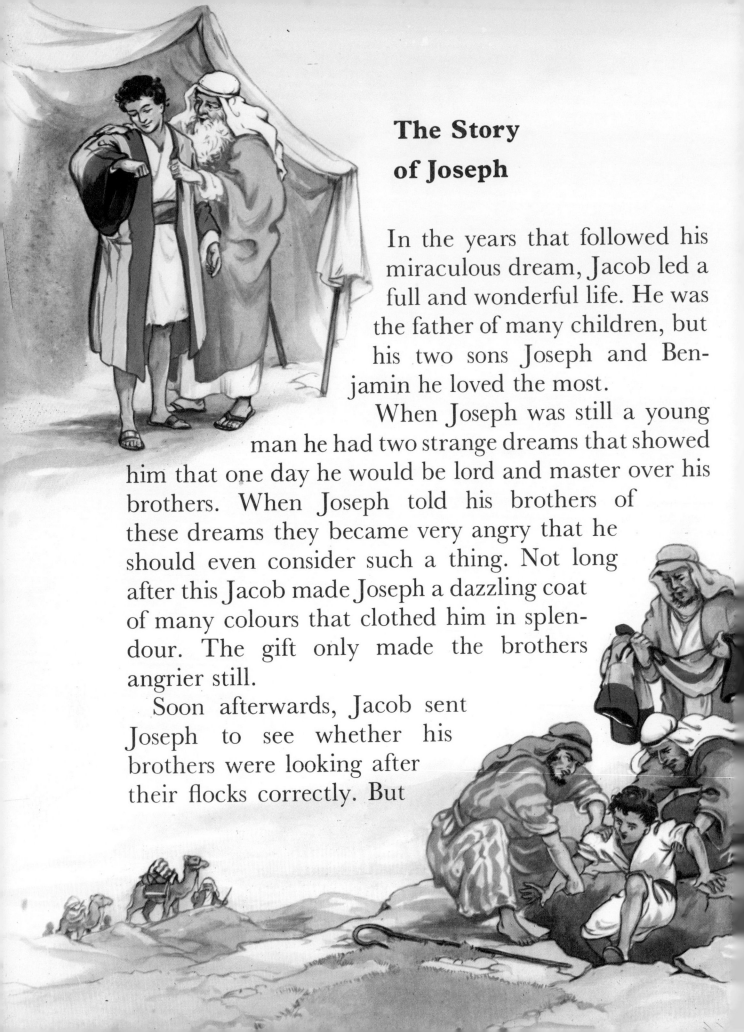

The Story of Joseph

In the years that followed his miraculous dream, Jacob led a full and wonderful life. He was the father of many children, but his two sons Joseph and Benjamin he loved the most.

When Joseph was still a young man he had two strange dreams that showed him that one day he would be lord and master over his brothers. When Joseph told his brothers of these dreams they became very angry that he should even consider such a thing. Not long after this Jacob made Joseph a dazzling coat of many colours that clothed him in splendour. The gift only made the brothers angrier still.

Soon afterwards, Jacob sent Joseph to see whether his brothers were looking after their flocks correctly. But when they saw Joseph the brothers decided to kill him.

One of the brothers, however, was against doing this and so they put Joseph into a pit instead. Finally poor Joseph was sold to some merchants passing on their way to Egypt.

Once in Egypt Joseph was sold as a slave, but before long his master unjustly imprisoned him. Fortunately, Joseph became well known in prison for being able to tell the meanings of strange dreams, for one day the king, or Pharaoh, had two dreams that none could explain.

Joseph was brought before the Pharaoh and told him that the dreams meant that Egypt was going to have seven wonderful harvests and then seven years of famine.

The Pharaoh was much concerned on hearing this and decided that Joseph should be in charge of all his kingdom. In the seven good years that followed Joseph stored up great supplies of corn so that when famine came there was still food in plenty.

One day Joseph's brothers came to buy corn in Egypt. On their arrival they were brought before Joseph. Being now a great lord, they bowed low before him. Joseph's dream had come true.

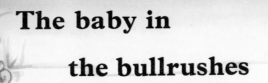

The baby in
the bullrushes

After Joseph died, his people, the Hebrews, became stronger and stronger. The Egyptians seeing this became much afraid and made the Hebrews slaves before they could grow more powerful. But even this did not stop their numbers growing, and so the Pharaoh of that time ordered that every Hebrew baby boy should be drowned.

One Hebrew mother loved her baby boy so much that she hid him in a basket by the riverside. Not long afterwards the daughter of the Pharaoh came down to the river to bathe and saw the basket hidden in the bullrushes. She decided to keep the little boy for her own but being a Hebrew baby she could not take him home to her father's palace. Instead, she asked the baby's own mother to care for him.

As soon as he was old enough the little boy went to live with the princess. She called him Moses and he was brought up as an Egyptian prince.

One day, when he had grown up, Moses saw an Egyptian beating a Hebrew slave. This made Moses so angry that he killed the Egyptian with one blow, and he had to flee.

For some time Moses lived in the desert. Then one evening a bush nearby him suddenly burst into flames—and yet it was not burnt! The voice of God then sounded forth from the heart of the bush. God told Moses that He had come to save the Hebrews from slavery and that Moses would be His messenger.

Taking his brother Aaron with him Moses went to Egypt. They told the Pharaoh that God had said that the children of Israel must be set free, but he only refused and made the Hebrews work harder still. God sent Moses and Aaron to see the Pharaoh a second time.

This time the Pharaoh asked Moses to prove that he was from God. Aaron threw down his staff and it turned into a serpent! When the Pharaoh saw this he commanded his own wise men to throw their staffs upon the ground. These too turned into serpents but Aaron's serpent ate them all up! Yet even with this sign the Pharaoh refused to free the children of Israel.

Moses leads the
people to freedom

God had promised the children of Israel that he would free them from captivity and take them into a land flowing with milk and honey. They must serve God and not the Pharaoh. Moses and Aaron were sent to the Pharaoh once again. Taking his staff into his hand, Moses stood before the wicked king and said: "The Lord God has sent me unto you saying let my people go." Then Aaron took his miraculous staff and turned all the water in Egypt into blood. The Pharaoh was still determined to keep the children of Israel slaves and it was not until God slew the eldest son in every Egyptian family that he finally agreed to set them free.

The Hebrews left at once. In all they were six hundred thousand strong with Moses and Aaron at their head. Hardly had they left Egypt, however, than the Egyptians changed their minds and sent a great army to bring them all back into captivity.

Before the Hebrews stood a great sea barring their way. Once more God came to their rescue. Moses lifted his wonderful staff over the sea and the waters rolled back making a dry way for the people to cross. The Egyptians chased after them, but although the sea kept back for the Hebrews it crashed down on the charging Egyptians and drowned every one.

The Journey through the desert

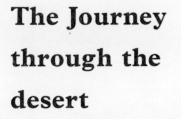

The journey of the children of Israel to the promised land took many years. God, however, was always near. He gave them food and water, and showed them the way.

God told Moses to build a place where He could always dwell among the people on their journey. The children of Israel were always moving, of course, and this house for God was built like a great tent so they could carry it with them.

It was called the tabernacle. In the middle was a smaller tent which held the most treasured belongings of the people, such as the ten commandments which God had given to Moses. These treasures were kept in the ark of the covenant. Only the finest things were used in making the tabernacle and when it was finished it was filled with the glory of God.

As they came near the promised land the children of Israel found the kingdom of King Balak barring their way. Balak knew that he could not defeat the Hebrews and so he called upon a wise man called

Balaam to lay a curse upon them.

On the journey to meet Balak, Balaam's ass ran off the road three times and Balaam beat the ass severly.

"What have I done," said the ass, "that you should beat me three times?" Then Balaam's eyes were opened and he saw an angel of the Lord before him. It had been the angel who had turned the ass from its path.

The angel told Balaam that he must only speak the words that God gave to him. And so it was that when he came to Balak he could not curse the children of Israel.

Instead he blessed them.

Many were the obstacles that had to be crossed before the promised land was reached. One of the greatest was when the children of Israel found their way blocked by the River Jordan. But God was always with them, and as the feet of the priests carrying the ark of the covenant touched the water the river dried up before them.

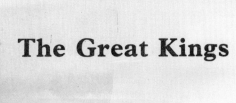

The Great Kings

The first king of Israel was Saul. He was not a very good king, however, and God chose a young man called David to be the next king.

David was bold and adventurous even as a young man and when he slew the famous giant Goliath with his sling he became the hero of the Israelites. This made Saul very jealous and David feared that Saul would try to kill him.

David's greatest friend was Saul's own son Jonathan and while David went into hiding Jonathan found out that David's fears were true. The very next day Jonathan went hunting near his friend's hiding place. Jonathan set an arrow to his bow, and shot it. As his servant boy ran to fetch it, Jonathan called out, "Make speed, haste, stay not!" This was the signal for David to flee. Saul hunted David for a long time, even though David tried to show him that he did not hate him. Once when David found Saul asleep and could easily have killed him, all he did was to cut a piece from his robe. In time Saul saw his mistake

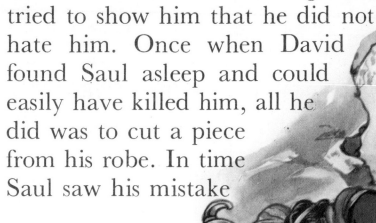

in being jealous of David.

Later, David became a great king although his son, Solomon, was greater still. Under Solomon's rule the children of Israel enjoyed a time of peace and happiness. And it was to Solomon that fell the task of building a magnificent temple to hold the ark of the covenant. By the time the temple was finished the fame of Solomon had spread far and wide. One of the greatest visitors to his court was the Queen of Sheba who was amazed by his great wisdom and understanding.

Elijah and Elisha

Not everyone in Israel had worshipped the idols of Queen Jezebel. A few of the people had never ceased to believe in God and one of these was young Elisha.

Elisha was ploughing in his father's fields one day when he saw Elijah, the great prophet, walking towards him. Elijah came up to the young farmer and as he passed he took his cloak and laid it upon Elisha's shoulders. Elijah wanted him to follow in his footsteps and carry on his work.

Leaving his oxen, Elisha ran after the prophet and asked if he could follow him. Then a strange thing happened. Elijah looked at him and said, "Go back again, for what have I done to you?" Elijah wanted to test Elisha to see if he understood in his heart the meaning of Elijah's sign. The young farmer did understand, however. He wanted to be with Elijah more than anything else in the world.

In the years that followed Elijah gave to his young servant and pupil the knowledge and understanding to help him to become a prophet.

On the day that Elijah knew they were to part, he asked Elisha what gift he would like. Elisha asked to inherit the spirit that had made Elijah so close to God. Then Elijah was carried up to heaven. Elisha saw him being carried up and in that moment he received Elijah's spirit. From that day Elisha was Israel's prophet.

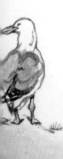

BIBLE STORIES

from the
New Testament

The First Christmas

Nearly two thousand years ago, a woman called Mary lived in the village of Nazareth, which is in the land of Palestine. One day an angel appeared to Mary. The angel told Mary that a baby who would be called Jesus, the Son of God, was to be born into the world and that she had been chosen to be the baby's mother.

Some time later, Mary and her husband Joseph, who was a carpenter, had to make a journey to the nearby city of Bethlehem. But when they arrived they found that every inn was full and they had to make their bed in a stable with the cattle. During this night Mary's baby was born. Then, because there was no proper cradle to put him in, Mary laid the baby Jesus in a manger.

The Good

Shepherds

While Mary was in the stable, gently caring for the newborn baby Jesus, some shepherds were minding their flocks not far away. Suddenly an angel of the Lord appeared to them in all his glory and the humble shepherds were much afraid. The angel, however, told them not to be afraid for he had good news to tell. A baby Saviour had been born that day and they were to search for him. They would find him lying in a manger, wrapped in swaddling clothes. Then the heavenly light died away and the shepherds left for Bethlehem at once, where they worshipped the baby Jesus.

The Three Wise Men

When Jesus was born in Bethlehem on that first Christmas day, three wise men were watching the night sky in a land far away. Suddenly, there appeared in the heavens a new and very bright star. In some wonderful way it showed the wise men that God had sent a Saviour unto the world. The wise men set off without delay to worship the baby Jesus, and after travelling over many lands arrived at Jerusalem. From there the star moved before them until it came to rest over the house where Jesus lay. The three wise men went straightway into the house and seeing the young Jesus and his mother, fell down and worshipped him.

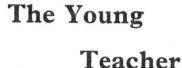

The Young Teacher

When Jesus was twelve years old, his parents took him to Jerusalem for one of the great festivals of their people. When the feast was over and Joseph and Mary left for home, Jesus stayed behind without their knowing it. When they realised that he was missing, Joseph and Mary returned to Jerusalem at once and after three days found him in the temple. There was the young Jesus in the midst of all the teachers and the wise men asking questions and listening carefully to what they said. Everyone who heard him was amazed at his knowledge.

Gathering the Disciples

The work of Jesus was to show people everywhere what the worship of God really meant. This was a huge task. Even Jesus could not do it all by himself and so he looked for men and women to help him. People who would help him while he was alive and carry on his teaching after he had gone.

These men were called disciples. Here is the wonderful way he gathered them together.

One day when he was walking by the sea shore he saw two fishermen casting their nets into the sea. "Follow me," said Jesus, "and I will make you fishers of men." The men, whose names were Peter and Andrew, left their nets at once and followed.

Later he found two other fishermen, James and John, mending their nets. Again he said, "Follow me." Another time he found a Customs officer at his work. This man's name was Matthew and, like many of the disciples, he too followed Jesus without delay.

The house built

on rock

When Jesus began teaching the true way of God, he did so in three simple ways. The first was by setting the highest example to people by the way he lived. The second was to heal the sick and help the poor.

The third way was to tell us how we should live and what the kingdom of heaven really meant. This third part of his work he often did by telling simple stories which are called parables. Jesus told these parables in such a way that even the most humble person could see their meaning. Here is one of them.

Jesus had been teaching the disciples some wonderful lessons. When he had finished he told them that a man who heard these sayings of his and carried them out was like a wise man who built his house upon a rock. Then when the storms came and the winds blew and the rain beat down, the house stood firm for its foundations were strong. It was like a man who believed in God.

Jesus then said that the man who heard his words and did not do as they bid was like a foolish man who built his house on sand. Then when the same storms beat on that house it tumbled to the ground for it had no foundations.

The parable of the
son who was lost

Jesus once told the story of a weal-
thy farmer who had two sons. One
day the youngest son asked his
father for his share of the family
fortune. Then he left home
and travelled to another country where
he foolishly wasted the money. Soon he
had none left. Before long famine came
to the country and without money the
young man was forced to become a
swineherd, for he could find no
other work. He even had to eat the
pig's food to stay alive. One day he
came to himself and realised that
many of his
father's servants

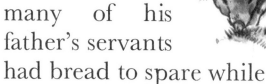

had bread to spare while
he was starving. And so he
went home. His father saw
him coming from afar and
ran to greet him. He was so
delighted, for this was his
own son who had been lost.

The parable
of the sower

This is one of Jesus's most famous parables. A sower went out to sow wheat. Some of the seed fell on the path and was eaten up by the birds. Other seed fell on stony soil. When this wheat grew its roots were shallow and it withered in the sun. There were thistles, too, around the field. Some of the seed fell among these, only to be choked by them. But some seed fell on good soil, grew strong and increased many times.

The disciples asked Jesus the meaning of this story and he told them that the seed was God's teaching. Some people heard it only to forget almost at once. Others accepted God's word gladly when they heard it, but like the seed on the stony soil it had not taken root.

The thistles were the cares and riches of the world which made people forget God. Only in the good soil did the seed multiply. This soil was the people who took God's word to their hearts and kept it there.

The sheep that was lost

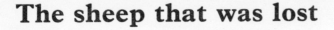

In his stories Jesus often spoke about shepherds and their sheep. One of these stories was about a shepherd who had one hundred sheep. Then came a night when one of the sheep went astray and lost itself.

The shepherd lost not a moment and left the ninety-nine sheep at once to search for the one that was lost. High and low searched the shepherd, into the mountains and in the valleys until at last he found it. The poor sheep had strayed into a rocky place and was so weak that it could not get back. If the shepherd had not found the sheep it may have been lost for ever.

Jesus said that he is the good shepherd and those who stray from God are the lost sheep.

Jesus also spoke of the kingdom of heaven. Once he spoke of it like this. There was a merchant who searched for fine pearls. Then he found the finest pearl he had ever seen in all his life. He wanted it so much that he sold everything so he could buy it.

Jesus
and the storm

Jesus spent much of his time teaching around the Sea of Galilee and he would often go from place to place by boat.

One such voyage he made on the evening of the day he had told the story of the sower and the seed. While the boat sailed calmly along, Jesus slept peacefully under the stars. Before long, however, a great storm blew up and the waves broke over the boat. Soon the storm reached such a peak that the disciples became afraid, even though Jesus slept quietly on. At last they were so afraid that they woke him and cried, "Lord save us, for we perish."

To this Jesus replied, "Why are you fearful, O you of little faith?" With this he arose and calmed the sea and the raging wind.

Feeding the multitudes

One day Jesus was followed into the country by a great crowd of five thousand people. The day drew on and it was clear to Jesus that the people were hungry for they had had no food. Jesus said to the disciples, "Give you them to eat," but they did not understand what he meant.

Then Andrew found a small boy who had brought a little food with him—five small loaves and two little fishes. Jesus took the loaves and fishes, looked to heaven and blessed them. Then he broke the food in pieces and gave it to the disciples. They in turn gave each person enough to feed them. Jesus had provided food for every single one and at the end there were twelve baskets over.

Martha and Mary

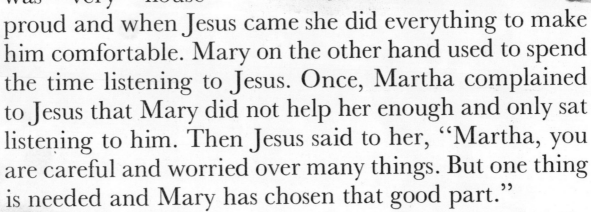

One of the many homes that Jesus used to stay at belonged to two sisters called Martha and Mary. Martha was very house-proud and when Jesus came she did everything to make him comfortable. Mary on the other hand used to spend the time listening to Jesus. Once, Martha complained to Jesus that Mary did not help her enough and only sat listening to him. Then Jesus said to her, "Martha, you are careful and worried over many things. But one thing is needed and Mary has chosen that good part."

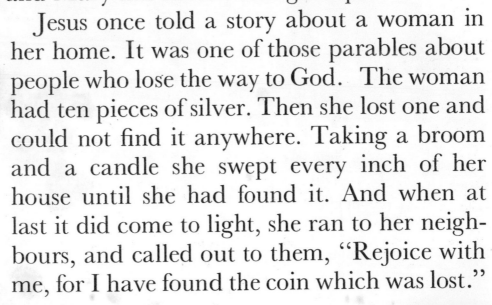

Jesus once told a story about a woman in her home. It was one of those parables about people who lose the way to God. The woman had ten pieces of silver. Then she lost one and could not find it anywhere. Taking a broom and a candle she swept every inch of her house until she had found it. And when at last it did come to light, she ran to her neighbours, and called out to them, "Rejoice with me, for I have found the coin which was lost."